BUT DAD!

BUT DAD!

GABRIEL FITZMAURICE
WITH ILLUSTRATIONS BY DONALD TESKEY

Children's
POOLBEG

Published in 1995
by Poolbeg Press Ltd
123 Baldoyle Industrial Estate
Dublin 13, Ireland

© Gabriel Fitzmaurice 1995

The moral right of the authors has been asserted.

A catalogue record for this book is available from the British Library.

ISBN 1 85371 453 4

Illustrations by Donald Teskey
Cover design by Poolbeg Group Services Ltd
Set by Poolbeg Group Services Ltd
Printed by The Guernsey Press Ltd,
Vale, Guernsey, Channel Islands.

For John and Nessa
from whom I stole these poems
all my love
from
Daddy Doodle

CONTENTS

BIFFETY BOFFETY BOO!

Biffety Boffety Boo!
I'm gonna tickle you.
Outa the bed
You sleepyhead.
Biffety Boffety Boo!

SEPTEMBER

We shouldn't go back in September –
September's the season of wasps:
No time for daydreaming
But squealing and screaming
At bob-and-weave wasps in the class.

We shouldn't go back in September –
September is berries-to-pick,
And while there is day
We should be out at play.
The thought of the school makes me sick.

HERE UP WALL

Humpty Dumpty was an egg,
Humpty Dumpty had no legs –
How did he get up the wall?
You don't need legs to climb at all!

MY SISTER

I got a little sister,
We got her just today;
Holy God sent her to us
Cos me and Mammy prayed

For a little girl to play with me,
A sister of my own;
Mam and Dad went somewhere
And brought my sister home.

She's so small you'd break her,
But she can cry real loud;
Mammy let me hold her
And I was awful proud.

I got a little sister,
We got her just today –
Soon she won't be bald at all
And she and I will play.

WATER BABIES

I'm a son
And you're a daughter
And we love
To mess with water
Shoes all squelchy
Hear them wheeze
Socks all sizzly
When we squeeze

WHY DOESN'T THE TEACHER BUY HIS OWN SCHOOL BOOKS?

Bookedy-bookedy-book-book-book!
Teacher says when he wants a look
And we hop up to give him the loan –
Why doesn't he go and buy his own?

CHUCK

I have a spaniel,
His name is Chuck –
We coulda called him Daniel,
Nathaniel or Huck;
But Chuck kinda suits him
With eyes like hope,
Ears like mittens
And nose of soap.

ONION EATER

I like to eat an onion
When I have a little drink –
I munch it like an apple,
And **BOY** does my breath stink!

Smoked Salmon

The fish! The fish!
Where his mouth?
The fish – he bite me, Mammy!
The fish he bold,
The fish he *BOLD* . . .
I like him –
In my tummy!

WHAT DADDY SAYS ABOUT US

Kids are so demanding
When they're *boy-ster-us* and shout
(At least you know what they're up to),
But when they're quiet
WATCH OUT!

SPIDER

Hairy spider on the wall!
John stiffens, John bawls;

Cool as you like while John fretted,
Nessa picked it up and ate it.

NESSA'S POME

Daddy write a pome
'Bout fish and spuds and peas
The fish no bitin' Nessa –
Daddy write it *please*!

What you doin' write that way?
Daddy do nothin' now.
What else will I put in, Nessa?
Santy and Dick's bow wow

And Mammy and John and Daddy
And horsey and Nessa too
And Jingle Bells and Santy.
That's all, Dad. Thank *YOU*!

STEALING SUGAR

Like dandruff on my daughter's lip,
Sandpaper on her chin
The sugar she's climbed up to whip
Is sweet. *How sweet?* As sin . . .

WHAT JOHN SAID

Daddy said he was sad
When Nessa got out of nappies

I said
We'll give her only one chance
And if she wets her knickers
She'll go right back into nappies again

SNOTS

Snots are gooey
Snots are sweet
Snots are chewy
Things to eat

WRITE THIS WAY

Copying from headlines,
I felt an awful twit
Cos I left out the "r" in *"shirt"*
And wrote *"s-h-i-t"*.

When the teacher was correcting,
He smiled at me and said,
"Read me what you've written –
What word is that?" he said.

I pointed with my finger,
Spelled out *"s-h-i-t"*
And everyone was laughing,
All that is – but me.

SCHOOL

Today the teacher asked me
Why I went to school –
"To learn big words," I stuttered.
(I don't know why I do . . .)

What is school for anyway?
You go five days a week
To sit, stand up when you are told,
To spell and write and speak

The right way.
But then, what use is that?
Cos all the people round here
Know exactly what

I'm sayin' an' I talkin' –
I don't need to learn
Words I'll never use again
When I leave school. I'm worn

From education
By the time it comes to three,
School is such a proper place;
But I'm mad about PE

And Art & Crafts and Drama,
Some poems are not too bad,
And Mam says 'tis no load to me
To read and write and add.

I'm bored at home on holidays,
I'm glad when school is back –
If school was run by children
'Twould be much better crack . . .

MAKING HER MARK

It's fun in Daddy's Diary
To scribble and to scrawl
But it's *gas* to make your squiggles
Squeak along the wall . . .

KISSING

When my sister goes on holidays
Dad says he's going to miss her;
I think I'm going to miss her too,
But I'm not going to kiss her.

It's fine to kiss your Mam and Dad –
In fact it's very good,
But I'm not going to kiss a girl
Although they say I should.

It's good to play with girls
Although you are a boy,
But when it comes to kissing them,
You get awful shy.
                    Oh boy!

ALL INSIDE A-BELLY

I couldn't eat my dinner once –
No matter how I tried,
All the meat and *poppies*
Wouldn't fit inside.

I couldn't eat my dinner once:
No matter what Mam'd do
To make it nice and yummy
(Like carrots in your stew),

I couldn't eat my dinner.
Now look what I ate –
All inside a-belly:
I ate up all my plate!

A *MILSEAN* FROM THE TEACHER

I want to go home! I want to go home!
I'm sick of all this schooling!
It's useless trying to cheer me up –
Who d'you think you're fooling?

milseán: a sweet

AUTUMN LEAVES

At first, all in a cluster,
They fidget on the ground,
Autumn in its party dress
Sizzling from its mound.

A wind strums out of Winter
And, whirling to its tune,
The dancers click their castanets
In a last flamenco. Soon

The dance is over,
The dancers lose their spark,
And, muffled by the Winter,
They limp around the park . . .

BIRTHDAYS

If you don't eat, you won't get big,
In fact, you'll get much thinner,
But I am getting very big
Because I eat my dinner.

I always eat my dinner now –
The more I eat, I know
The sooner my birthday comes
Because I'll grow and grow.

My birthday's coming sooner
And that will be a treat –
I'll have *two* birthdays every year
Because of all I eat!

SHOWER

I thought the roof was leaking
And I folded to a cower,
But I was awful silly –
I'd just set off the shower!

It spattered down upon me
Till I turned off the jet;
I told no one about it
Cos I wasn't very wet.

27

HIDIES

I go hide in Nessa's room
Daddy play *Cuck-oo*
Daddy no look in Nessa's room
Till Nessa say *Cuck-oo*.

Cuck-oo Daddy *Cuck-oo* Daddy
Daddy come find me –
Well now, where is Nessa?
Where can Nessa be?

She's not in Mammy's bedroom
Not in the study, no!
She's not in the sitting-room –
Where did Nessa go?

I think I know where Nessa is
(Someone's laughing, too) –
I'm going to catch that laughing:
Here it is – *Cuck-oo*!

HOW HIGH?

How high can I piddle?
– Higher than the door?
But the piddle hit it halfways up
And dribbled on the floor.

I got a ball of tissue
And rubbed the door till dry
And soaked it off the lino.
Wow! I can piddle high!

WALKING WITH JOHN

Humpty Dumpty sat on the wall
Hand on the wall
My hand on the wall
Isn't it scrumptious to rub off the wall
All the way off home

Home is for *goo-goos**
Hand on the wall
My hand on the wall
Daddy and me for *goo-goos* and tea
All the way off home

Off of the path
And on to the path
Hopping and stopping
Off of the path
And on to the path
All the way off home

Knock on the door
Hand on the door
Rubbing it
Rubbing
It's grand to be four
Goos-goos are ready for me and for Daddy
All the way off home

Goo-goos are crumbly
And squelchy
And fumbly
Goo-goos are good for me
for tea

Humpy Dumpty sat on the wall
Hand on the wall
My hand on the wall
All the way off home

goo-goos: eggs

"ME SICK TOO"

"John, you've got a temperature!
Take some *Calpol* – do!"
Nessa eyes him jealously
And whimpers, "Me sick too".

"Nessa, you don't need *Calpol* –
Nessa isn't sick";
Spring-loaded, Nessa bunches up
And triggers off a kick.

Her fists all in a fury,
She torrents out her woe,
Then turns and leaves me standing with,
"Nessa no want it. NO!"

DADDY'S CLEAN CLOTHES

Daddy is nicer in dirty clothes
Than he is when they are clean –
It's not that he *looks* nicer
But he doesn't act as mean.

Wash your hands! Don't touch me!
I've just put on clean clothes!
Don't kiss me with that jammy mouth
Or with that snotty nose!

Daddy is nicer in dirty clothes
Than he is when they are clean –
He's much more fun in dirty clothes
And he doesn't act as mean.

IF . . .

If I should get a brand-new gun
And then if I should drop it
And if the laser lit no more
What should I do? I'd swap it!

MATTRESS

Bouncy bouncy mattress!
Bouncy bouncy bed!
Upsy Daisy – all fall down!
Bouncing on my head.

Bouncy bouncy mattress!
Bouncy bouncy bed!
When you try to push it down,
It pops you up instead.

Bouncy bouncy mattress!
Bouncy bouncy bed!
Space must be a mattress
Because I've heard it said

That everything pops up in space
(Like I do in my bed!) –
The more you try to squeeze it down,
The more you fly instead!

NESSA DISCUSSES HER BROTHER

Boy!
What can I say about *Boy*?

He won't let me kiss him.
I like to kiss him
Before I pull his hair
Or kick him . . .
He's my brother
Mammy says
I shouldn't kick him.
But I love to swing my leg
Back and over
Up and down
Thunk!

Boy wears no nappy
But I do.
He wets into the toilet
Or anywhere he likes.
When I take off my nappy
To copy him,
I wet into my shoe.
Wet! Wet!
(I can say that)
And Mammy changes me.
Daddy does too.
It's nice to have your nappy changed,
Be buttered up with goo . . .

But *Boy* plays with me –
Up and down the hallway
Run and crawl and skip:
The carpet's nice and cushion-y
When you slip.

Sometimes *Boy* pushes me
And I howl and scream
And then *Boy* runs away from me
And hides out in his room.

Boy is my brother
(What's a brother, Dad?)
Someone who won't let me up
When *he's* got Mammy's lap . . .

THE BOY OF THE BARTONS

There was a boy of the Bartons
And when he was very young
He never shut up talking
And the Devil cut off his tongue.

GOOD DOGGIE!

Nessa bites him first
Then kisses,
Rubs his ears
Then thumps,
Pulls his tail
And pokes his eye,
Tickles him.

The chump
Licks her face
And nuzzles her,
Wags his tail
And sniffs.
Oh, love has no defences:
The things we do for kids!

HELLO FLY

Hello fly

My name is John
I won't kill you

You're a small fly
Not a big fat bee
That would sting me
(I don't like the big fat bee –
He frightens me)

Fly
Will you play with me?
Round and round the footpath
Watch me run and run
Round and round come catch me!
It's fun

Fly
Why don't you move when I touch you?
Are you dead?
I can push you with my finger
On the window ledge

Slowly off you stagger
Off
Off
Off
Up Granda's wall

Goodbye fly
See you 'morrow
Sure we're not dead at all

THE MAN FROM *DEN TV*

I waited for the man to ring me
The man from *Den TV*;
I stood on a chair beside the phone
And hopped excitedly.

I waited for the man to ring me;
I thought that he would call
Cos the man said he'd ring some kids,
But he never rang at all.

I heard it on the telly,
They said that they would call;
Even people on the telly
Can make you want to bawl.

But I didn't bawl at all.

ME AND MY TURTLE CAP

Áine was in the Final,
We went to cheer and clap,
I went along with Daddy,
And wore my Turtle Cap.

The show began at seven,
I sat in Daddy's lap,
There was singing, acts and dancing
And I left on my cap.

Then we went behind the stage
And the MC said "Good chap,
You can introduce her,
You and your Turtle Cap?"

She brought me out on to the stage,
The whole place cheered and clapped
When I said "Áine from Moyvane"
And scratched my Turtle Cap!

I went behind the curtain
And sat in Daddy's lap,
Daddy-Doodle rubbed my head
And knocked off my Turtle Cap!

OPERATION

They took out my tonsils
And my adenoids (I suppose)
Cos when I woke next morning
I was ntalking nthrough ny nose.

It wasn't like my real voice –
The words fizzed up and up,
But I got lumps of ice cream
    And loads of *7-Up*.

And Daddy said my talking
    Was hard to understand,
    But my operation's over
    And everything is grand.

Steppin' in Your Shadow

I'm steppin' in your shadow, Dad!
Don't walk, son, in the dark.
Out into the sunshine
And run around the park.

I'm steppin' in your shadow, Dad!
You're treading on my heels
Out into the sunshine
And run around the fields.

I'm steppin' in your shadow, Dad!
I'm blinded by the sun!
Of a sudden, he lets go
And breaks into a run.

47

BUT DAD!

John pick up those pencils
Put 'em in your bag
You're strewing the place with rubbish
Pick 'em up **BUT DAD** . . .

John put the milk back in the fridge
The sun will turn it bad
Take that jug down from your mouth
You're spilling it **BUT DAD** . . .

John it's time to go to bed
Beddy-byes **BUT DAD** . . .
I'M NOT SLEEPY I'LL BE GOOD
MY HEART WILL MAKE ME SAD
OH ABRACADABRA JESUS
INTERCEDE WITH DAD

RELIGION CLASS

"Jesus suffered awful pain
When the spear pierced through His side,
The nails, the whips, the crown of thorns,
When He was crucified.

But Jesus suffered inner pain –
The jeers, the ruination . . .
Do you ever suffer inner pain?"
"WHEN YOU GET CONSTIPATION!"

HALLOWE'EN

Hallowe'en is scary –
At least those big hairy masks are:
Your heart starts to wallop,
Your skin starts to crawl
Even though you know
The person inside isn't a witch at all.

51

NATURE WALK

Sonny just loves Nature Walks
Sloshing through the grass –
They're better than hot afternoons
Fettered in the class.

He picked a mace of buttercup,
Some fern-webs, a rose;
The fool! He picked a nettle –
And then he picked his nose!

Yes! Sonny just loves Nature Walks
Prowling through the woods
Approved at last by teacher,
The only time he's "good"!

A HAIRY STORY

Benny Barber's hair sticks out
Like two wings that flap about.

His hair's OK when he goes to bed
But every morning on his head

The wings have curled up again –
No comb or scissors flattens them.

I think that we should shave his hair,
But Benny Barber doesn't care!

WHY IS AUSTRALIA EIGHT HOURS AHEAD OF US?

Why is Australia eight hours ahead of us?
Because Santa comes.
(It takes him eight hours to come from Australia.)
So now!
You don't believe in Santa –
So why is Australia eight hours ahead of us?
How does he come down the chimney?
He turns into dust.
Santa's magic
You're tragic . . .
Why is Australia eight hours ahead of us?

AN APPLE FOR THE TEACHER

"Bring apples to eat", the teacher said,
But me, I'd rather mush
So I threw mine down the toilet
But the apple wouldn't flush.

It just kept bobbing like a ball
As the flush foamed all about,
So I put my hand in the toilet bowl
And took the apple out.

I washed it in the basin
So nobody would know
Then dried it on my jumper
And gave it to Mister O

(That's what we call our teacher);
He rubbed it once or twice
And then he ate my apple
He said 'twas very nice.

CHRISTMAS IS COMING

Where *Jingle Bells* go home to Mammy?
– *Jingle Bells* go moon?
Jingle Bells gone home to Mammy
– *Jingle Bells* come soon!

"Mommy"

We call our teacher "Miss"
But one day little Tommy
Forgot what he should call her
And he called her "Mommy"!

And when he said it we all laughed,
He was a silly bunny
But Tommy only laughed as well –
He thought 'twas awful funny.

THE JUMBLE SALE

There was a Jumble Sale in school – 'twas on this
        morning
I had a pound to spend it just on me,
I went to the Sale with Jim and all my classmates
And swapped my pound with Jim for 20p.

I bought a colour Aston Villa poster,
A cup of *Coke*, then I ran out of cash –
There were lots of other things there that I wanted
So I went to Jim to get my money back.

But he had bought a Man. United poster,
A book, a jigsaw and tons of other toys;
When I saw all he had, I started bawling
And teacher gave me a hankie to wipe my eyes.

He told us to go off, sort out our problem –
Jim gave me back the money in his hand,
A comic and the Man. United poster.
We're friends again, and everything is grand.

ACT OF SORROW

Once we were playing football
And Bob tripped me. So I placed
The ball down for a free
And kicked it in his face.

I said I didn't mean it
But he knew I lied –
He looked at me, his cheek all red;
And then he cried.

I blazed it with my instep,
It landed on his cheek –
If all my shots were as accurate
We'd win out every week.

But Bob just cried and held his face,
And when I saw him there
Surrounded by his team-mates,
Well, I just didn't care

If we never won another match
Cos I had hurt my friend;
I cried and said "I'm sorry"
And Bob held out his hand.

Ashamed, ashamed I shook his hand,
The best friend that I've got –
I'll kick no more balls in his face.
But, boy, it was some shot.

SANTA CLAUS

Santa Claus is coming
To the village hall;
I'm going to see Santa Claus
And I won't cry at all.

Hello Santa! This is me!
(Oh Dad, he's awful hairy!
Oh Dad, don't let him near me!
Oh Dad, he's awful scary!)

Santa Claus was here today
In the village hall –
He gave me crisps and lemonade
(All I could do was bawl).

NESSA'S TROLLEY

I'd rather use my kitchen as a trolley
Than play with dollies.

You take off the cooker part,
The cupboard part, the sink part;
The bottom is a trolley –
That's the part that I like best.

I found out about the trolley
Before we'd taken down the holly
Or the crib.

I stand upon my trolley
Gingerly and jolly
And John pushes me around the house.

It's fun up on my trolley
It's not like *Pretty Polly*
Or *Dressing Up Your Dolly*
But it's jolly on my trolley.

Hup there Molly!
Hup!
Hup!

KNOWING

Four o'clock this morning
In the middle of the night
I couldn't see my fingers
And I couldn't find the light
My son asleep beside me
Was tugging at my hair
And because of his tug-tugging
I knew that I was there

NEWSFLASH

"Did you hear *The News* this morning?
It's in the paper too –
Here it is, I'll read it
(I'm not joking you):

Santa can't come this Christmas!
His reindeer got a puncture –
He's in Ballyhahill hospital.
They've no comment at this juncture."

Daddy isn't smiling
But he can't fool me –
I'll ring up the hospital
And *then* we'll see . . .

65

"YOU'LL THANK ME YET"

Why is it that what's good for me
Is yuck or hard or boring?
Grown-ups say "You'll thank me yet" –
Enough to put you snoring.

I know they're right, but it makes me mad
That I haven't any say –
"Do this! Do that!", they never stop;
They tell me *when to play*!

When I'm grown and have kids of my own,
I'll be a better Dad –
Everyone will have a say
And my kids won't grow up mad.

THE CLOWN

The circus came,
The circus came,
The circus came to town,
And Daddy drove me in to it
But when I saw the clown,
I froze right in my footsteps
Then thawed out to a scream –
Even Daddy couldn't save me.

Even now, I dream
Of things no one can save me from,
That nothing takes away,
Things that terrify at night
But also in the day –

Like that clown in Duffy's Circus
While others roared in glee,
I roared out in terror
For he was part of me . . .

WHERE ARE YOU, PAUDIE PELICAN?

Where are you, Paudie Pelican?
Please sir, here.
You're not, I fear.

Are you in Tokyo?
Please sir, no.
In Camelot?
Sir, I'm not.
Are you in Clare?
Please sir, I'm not there.

You're not in Tokyo, Camelot, Clare –
Then you must be somewhere else.

Yes, sir.

Paudie, dear –
If you're somewhere else
YOU CAN'T BE HERE!

NIGHTMARE

Small boy
Doesn't know he's dreaming

Gates close around him
He can't scream
He tries to run
But cannot move
It's gaining

It doesn't vanish
When he wakes out of the dream

POWER CUT IN THE NORTH POLE

Power Cut in the North Pole!
Rudolf's nose won't light.
Will the elves charge up his nose
In time for Christmas night?

Without his nose to light them,
Will the reindeer find their way?
Rudolf's nose is flat, won't shine –
Who will guide the sleigh?

Daddy's only joking,
He's always playing tricks.
Rudolf's nose – it glows and glows:
No need to have it fixed.

MONKEY

They've come to see a monkey –
It means I must be funny,
Do what they expect of me
Because they've paid their money.

There are times I just can't do it
(They note it, pass me by),
Times I must compose myself
As the parrots squawk "Goodbye."

SNOW

The sky is turned upside-down
And clouds are rolling
On the ground.

Roofs are ice cream,
Trees are cones,
I'm a Dragon spitting smoke.

On a froth-white beach
Of freezing sand
Footfalls crack like withered leaves
Crushed in fireblue hands.

MY HURLEY

Left! Right! Left! Right!
Marching down the hall,
My hurley as a rifle.
About turn at the wall!

I'm a soldier, Mammy.
(A hurley's best by far –
Today it can be a gun,
Tomorrow a guitar).

HALF PAST CLOCK

When I wake him in the morning,
Put on his shoes and socks,
He moans that it's too early –
That it's only half past clock.

And when he's outside playing
And I say it's time to lock
The house up, that it's bedtime,
It's only half past clock.

I've rummaged through psychology,
Rifled *Dr Spock*
But I cannot find an answer
To *it's only half past clock.*

I'll turn the tables on him
 – He'll get an awful shock –
Explain that once he's said it,
It's no longer *half past clock.*

And then we'll be the poorer
Measuring tick-tock –
Time is what we make it:
Hurrah for *half past clock!*

I FELL OFF MY PLATFORMS

I fell off my platforms
And now I'm limping round,
And everybody notices.
Because of this, I've found

I'm the centre of attention
(My ankle's really sore),
And when they fail to notice me,
I limp a little more!

THE POSTMAN

It's storming out
It's storming out
It's storming out today
The postman gives his letters out –
I hope they don't blow away.

It's storming out
It's storming out
It's storming out today
The postman gives his letters out –
I hope *he* doesn't blow away!

WHERE BABIES COME FROM

Babies grow in a lady's heart
That's where babies come from
You get babies from the stork
That's where babies come from . . .

Babies grow in a lady's heart
You've seen it on TV
You get babies from the stork
Whichever can it be?

You know you know a baby,
It tugs, it kicks, it sucks,
The myth of its beginning
Won't change how it works.

Babies are and whence they come
Doesn't really matter:
From a lady's heart or from the stork –
It's not about to shatter

The way you know what babies are:
Two stories – no big deal!
The baby is the story
And the baby's real!

SILENT NIGHT

Christmas Night in Bethlehem,
The little children draw
Jesus, Mary, Joseph,
An ox, an ass, some straw,
And a roly-poly gentleman –
The teacher asks, "Who's this?"
One child looks up and answers her:
"That's Round John Virgin, miss."

DINOSAUR

I brought my dinosaur to school –
It was a Brontosaurus;
I played with it with my friend Jim,
But then the teacher saw us.

"Put that thing in", the teacher said,
"Or I'll put it in my drawer":
He only saw a plastic toy,
But I could hear it roar.

BEEBLA

(for John and Nessa)

Beebla wasn't sure that he was born
(What was it to be born? He didn't know),
But his mother had been dying four or five times:
Beebla threatened God: "Don't let her go –
If You do, then I won't say my prayers;
If You do, then I won't go to Mass."
The priest came and anointed Beebla's Mammy.
Next morning, Beebla boasted in his class:
"My mother was anointed in the night-time;
The priest came to our house, I stayed up late."
Beebla was cock-proud of his achievement:
All the class was listening – this was great!

Beebla played with all the boys at playtime
(The girls were in the school across the way) –
They played football with a sock stuffed with old papers,
He'd forget about his Mammy in the play.
But always at the back of all his playing,
He knew about anointing in the night,
And, knowing this, there could be no unknowing –
Nothing in the world would change that quite.

Beebla got a motor-car in London –
A blue one with pedals which he craved
(Beebla'd been in hospital in London,
And, coming home, he'd had to have his way);
So his Daddy bought him his blue motor-car,
He drove it all the way out to the 'plane,
And touching down, cranky with excitement,
He squealed till he was in his car again.

He drove around the village, a born show-off;
He pulled into a funeral, kept his place,
And all the funeral cars, backed up behind him,
Couldn't hoot, for that would be disgrace!
He drove off from the Chapel to the graveyard,
And, tiring, he pulled out and headed back;
When his mother heard about it, she went purple
And grabbed for her *wallop-spoon* to smack;
But his Daddy shielded Beebla from her wallops –
They brushed across his Daddy's legs until
His mother's rage fizzled to a token:
She shook the spoon, and threatened that she's kill
Him if he didn't mind his manners;
But Beebla went on driving, till one day
A real car almost hit him at the Corner:
For safety, they took his car away.

Beebla didn't cry or throw a tantrum –
He knew that but for luck he would be dead,
And at night-time, after kisses, hugs and lights-out,
He started up his car inside his head.

Beebla got a piano once from Santa –
He ran down to the Church on Christmas Day
Before his Mammy or his Daddy could contain him
(He wanted all the crowd to hear him play).
And he walloped notes and pounded them and
thumped them
As *Silent Night* became a noisy day,
But it was *his* noise, all his own and he could make it –
It said things for him that only it could say.

And he stole into the Church another morning
When all the crowd had scattered home from Mass,
And he went up to the *mike* like Elvis Presley
But he only made an echo – it was off!
So Beebla went back home to his piano,
To the sound of what it is to be alone
Cos Beebla had no brothers or no sisters
And he often had to play all on his own.

Beebla was the crossest in the village –
He was not afraid of beast or man:
He'd jump off walls, climb trees, walk under horses –
He did it for a dare; until the Wren
When the Wren Boys dressed up in masks and sashes
And came into your house to dance and play –

Beebla was excited at the Wren Boys,
He simply couldn't wait for Stephen's Day;
But when the Wren Boys came to Beebla's kitchen
Like horrors that he dreaded in his dreams,
He howled, tore off into the bathroom,
And hid behind the bath and kicked and screamed.
His mother came and told him not to worry,
Brought Tom Mangan in to him without the mask –
Tom Mangan was his friend, worked in the Creamery,
But today Tom Mangan caused his little heart
To pound inside his ribcage like a nightmare,
Was fear dressed up and playing for hard cash –
Tom would be his friend again tomorrow,
But today Beebla hung around the bath.

He ran away from school the day he started –
He ran before he got inside the door
And his friends who'd brought him there that morning
Couldn't catch him. But he'd no time to explore
The village that morning in December
Before Christmas trees were common, or lights lit –
Beebla had to figure out his problem
And he wasn't sure how he'd get out of it.

He stole into his shop and no one noticed
(His Daddy's shop, his Mammy wasn't well)
And he hid beneath the counter till Daddy found him:
"Oh Daddy, Daddy, Daddy, please don't tell
Mammy that I ran from school this morning –
The doors were big and dark, the windows high;

And Dad, I ran from school this morning
– I had to – 'twas either that or cry".
His Daddy didn't mind, his Mammy neither,
He stayed at home till Eastertime, and then
One morning he got dressed-up, took his schoolbag,
Brushed his hair, and went to school again.

He played with all the boys in *The Back Haggarts*,
A place that has no name (it's gone!) today,
High jumps, long jumps, triple jumps and marbles,
But there was one game not everyone could play –
The secret game that he was once allowed in:
Doctors, where you pulled down your pants
To be examined by one who was "The Doctor";
Beebla ran when asked to drop his pants!
And they chased him, calling him "a coward",
But Beebla didn't want to play that fun
(Mostly cos a girl was "The Doctor"!)
He ran in home but didn't tell anyone.

And one time, too, he fought a boy for nothing
Cos the older boys had goaded them to fight;
After that, he never fought for nothing
Cos he knew inside himself it wasn't right.

Beebla would annoy you with his questions –
He wanted to know everything, and why:
Why he was, what was it to be *Beebla*,
And would his mother live, or would she die?
And what was it to die? Was it like *Cowboys*

Where you could live and die and live again?
Or would Mammy be forever up in Heaven?
(Forever was how much times one-to-ten?)

This was all before the television,
About the time we got electric light,
Before bungalows, bidets or flush-toilets,
Where dark was dark, and fairies roamed the night.
This story's a true story – *honest Injun*!
You tell me that it's funny, a bit sad;
Be happy! It has a happy ending
Cos Beebla grew up to be your Dad.

KISSES

A kiss! A kiss! Give us a kiss!
Because I'm small, they go on like this;
Everyone asking me to kiss 'em.
No more kisses! (And I won't miss 'em!)